Published in Great Britain in 1995 by

Colin Baxter Photography Ltd
Grantown-on-Spey
Scotland PH26 3NA

Text © Roy Dennis
All rights reserved

atalogue record for this book is available from the British Library

ISBN 0-948661-62-3

Front Cover Photograph: Neil McIntyre
Back Cover Photograph: Colin Baxter

The
BIRD
of Badenoch & St

A CIP